*Become
an
Elite
Mental
Athlete*

BECOME AN ELITE
MENTAL
ATHLETE

Commit to Building Your Brain and
Improving Your Mental Game

Become an Elite Mental Athlete

by David Silverstein

Published by Breakthrough Performance Press
1200 17th St., Suite 180
Denver, CO 80202

Editor: Jessica Harper
Designers: Stacy Howard, Luke Van Deman
Illustrator: Josh Abraham

ISBN-13: 978-1-938353-03-1

Printed in the United States of America

Contents

INTRODUCTION

This book is one I have looked forward to writing for several years. It represents the convergence of a number of observations, experiences, and lots of research. The concept is derived from my thinking about what it means for us to live in a "knowledge" economy or the "information" age.

Living in Boulder, Colo.—a prime Olympic training ground and home to many world-class athletes—I've become familiar with the kind of training elite athletes subject themselves to. So for some reason…I don't really recall why…I asked myself one day, "Why is it that the best athletes in the world are always working at becoming even better athletes, yet the best thinkers in the world don't work on becoming better thinkers?"

Now, to begin addressing that question, it's important that I provide some context for what working to get better really means. Let's take a world-class basketball player like LeBron James, who many argue is the best in the world and some even think the best that's ever played the game. What does LeBron James do to get better at basketball? Presumably, some combination of many things including working on his vertical leap, his strength, his flexibility, his reflexes, his inside shooting, his outside shooting, his ball handling, his nutrition, his sleep, and his stress control. What LeBron James doesn't do is simply head out and play some pickup basketball.

Next, we could ask ourselves, "What does LeBron James do to get ready for a big game?" Presumably he studies the players on the other team, discusses strategy for the game with his coach and teammates, eats a nutritious meal, perhaps carb loads for energy, gets a good night's sleep, warms up before the game, and so on.

The question that struck me was, "If the best of the best—a player like LeBron James—does all that to prepare himself to be a winner at basketball, why don't the best of the best thinkers in the world work just as hard at improving their mental abilities? Why don't they exercise their brains, focus on their sleep and nutrition, and prepare for a big meeting or negotiation with the same kind of rigor and focus as LeBron James preparing for a big game?"

There are many people in all kinds of positions who rely on their brains to excel at their craft. And to win—whether an election debate, a business negotiation, or a new product design—they need to be better than their opponents. They need to ensure that their brains are kept in peak condition.

At BMGI, our work in the areas of innovation and strategy has frequently taken us somewhere we didn't expect. While researching tools and methods that could be used by our clients in the context of facilitated workshops, we constantly found ourselves back in the same place—the brain. We came to understand that, for better or worse, most of the work of real innovative and strategic thinking didn't happen in our workshops. Most of it happened at night, between about 10 p.m. and 6 a.m. Some of it also happened in the shower or when out on a long run. Yet, despite realizing that most of what our clients needed didn't happen in their meetings with us, we also realized that we could still help them in many, many ways. For example, as discussed in my prior book, *One Dot, Two Dots, Get Some New Dots*, we could help our clients fill their heads with lots of context so their brains would have more dots to connect during their dot connection time. We could also help them make sense of their dots and their dot connections. And, finally, we realized that we could help them learn how to maximize their brains' own power through many of the things covered in this book.

To get the most out of this book, there's one thing that I think is very important: Reading it cover to cover. Although you can jump to the things you are most interested in learning about, it's very important that you read all the sections so you truly understand how to "prepare for the big game." That's the only way you will gain a holistic perspective on how to build your body and mind so you can become an elite mental athlete. Another important point to get the most from this book: You must be in a position to believe the things you read. But once you take in some of the science—there's a cursory coverage of research in each chapter— believing becomes something that you can't avoid.

So, please enjoy the rest of the book, and most importantly, please take something away that helps you make change in your life.

Happy reading…

David Silverstein

ELITE PERFORMANCE

What does it take to be truly great? How do the star professionals in any field rise to the top? Let's start by looking at one of my personal favorite sports, basketball, to see what we can learn about elite performance.

Superstars of Professional Basketball

Think about the life of a professional basketball player. The players dash across the court, fire passes to teammates, jump vertical, dunk baskets. Sure, they're born with some natural gifts—height, fast reflexes—but the ones that make it to the NBA do much more. They work hard to both enhance their game-playing skills and build their bodies to meet the demands of the game. They make a conscious choice to leave their comfort zone. They push further, and they push consistently—not just occasionally—to excel.

Kobe Bryant's 666 Routine

Take a look at Kobe Bryant's 666 workout plan—six hours a day six days a week for six months. And that's just his personal body workout routine, which doesn't include all the time he spends at team practices, studying game videos, team strategy sessions, or the actual games.

Kobe varies his runs from slower, long distance (3 to 5 miles) to high-interval intensity training (HIIT), which usually consists of rapid short sprints. On the HIIT days, he varies the workouts so that his body does not get used to one set of stimuli.

He also does a lot of weight lifting, again maintaining variety in the types of exercises and what muscles he's targeting.

Kobe gears his workout to building the particular muscles and muscle exertion patterns needed for basketball. That's why he does squats, calf raises, and power cleans, which build explosiveness for sprinting and jumping. The rest of his workout is tailored to improving his size and strength, which allow him to slash to the basket or post up on other players.[1]

Pushing the Limits, Mixing It Up

Others, like LeBron James and Chris Paul, push for additional workouts, not just individually and with their team, but with personal coaches like Idan Ravin.

Interestingly, Ravin never played basketball professionally. But because of the unique workouts he designs and the skills he helps players build, he's been nicknamed "The Hoops Whisperer."

Why do players opt for the extra training, if they're already great? Ravin explains: "Guys like LeBron can cut all the corners and still get an A on the exam. Eighty percent of Chris Paul or LeBron is better than 99 percent of anyone else. But I ask them, 'What if you maximized it? What if you were 99 percent? Isn't that interesting?' I try to intrigue them. I say, 'What if?'"[2]

Ravin pushes LeBron not just through grueling conditioning and intricate ball-handling exercises, but beyond them. He literally throws anything at players to toughen their mental side as well. For example, Ravin sets up 13 cones within the key, to the top of the circle, and has players dribble among the cones without hitting them.[3] Sounds easy enough. But Ravin adds twists: Players have to dribble two balls at once, bouncing one high and the other low, moving forward and backward. Other times he throws tennis balls at them that they must catch while dribbling one ball.

Notice that Kobe, LeBron, and other stars don't just improve their game by practicing their game. They look deeper to improve their human machinery that enables them to achieve elite performance. They build their strength, explosive power, and agility to give them the core tools to excel on game day.

This preparation gets players ready to expect the unexpected and deal with whatever comes, all the while performing their best. I've been talking about basketball, but it's the same in business, where executives have so many factors to manage at once. Luckily, in business you don't have to react instantly, but you do have to juggle all the factors and make decisions under uncertainty and time-sensitive competitive conditions.

Superstars of Professional Business

There's really not much difference between professional sports and pro-fessional business. They are both highly competitive human endeavors in which the best of the best rise to the top. Natural acumen is great, but the best of the best know they can't just rely on natural talent; they need to develop their skills. In business, that means staying on top of current events, reading about new developments, being intellectually curious about what's going to happen next, and responding to a dynam-ic economy in the best way possible. But none of the strategic insight, situational awareness, and fast response is possible without a brain that is developed and sharpened for business.

Brain Training

We train our physical bodies to excel at physical tasks, why not train our minds to excel at mental tasks? A finely tuned mind is today's most important asset. Elite athletes know their bodies and train their bodies; elite mental athletes must know their brains and train their brains.

Just as athletes know they need to develop their physical muscles to excel in competition, so too, business professionals need to de-velop their mental muscles to excel in competition. There is solid evidence that the brain is in fact like a muscle—you can improve your brain's performance.

Elite athletes commit serious time to intentional improvement pro-grams, not just haphazard training. They work with a coach, diagnose skill levels, learn which muscles to work on, and how much. Likewise, this book will help you to improve your mental game. As business lead-ers, we all need to think about our mental goals and work toward them so that we don't atrophy. CEOs especially need to be elite mental ath-letes. They are being paid to lead the company, but they often don't think about training their minds the way athletes train their bodies.

This book will show you how you can improve your mental fitness, just like you can improve your physical fitness. Through exploring the latest research from cognitive science and neuroscience, we'll see documented results of what can be done—and has been done—to improve individuals' brain performance, even raising intelligence that was previously believed to be innate.

Why Do It?

You can train yourself to stretch your memory and tighten your attention. The reason to do this training, simply put, is that your competitors will be doing it, even if you aren't. Not only is it important for you personally in your career, but as a leader, your mind is the value you are bringing to a company. Improving your mind raises the value of your company. Helping your team improve their minds improves everyone's productivity and engagement. Finally, the benefits you gain also translate into personal well-being, such as reducing your chances of getting Alzheimer's disease and experiencing cognitive decline as you age. In the following chapters, we'll look more in-depth at the "why" and also the "how" of training your brain.

2

THE BRAIN: DID YOU KNOW?

Just as an elite physical athlete needs to understand how muscles, tendons, joints, and bones interconnect to form a coordinated high-performance physical machine, the elite mental athlete needs to understand how the brain's systems interconnect to form a coordinated high-performance mental machine. Weakness in any one area can lead to imbalanced performance.

Seeing the Brain in Action

Medical science has uncovered the biomechanics and biochemistry of muscles. Similarly, recent advances in neuroscience have uncovered myth-busting truths about the functioning of the brain.

Through PET (positron emission tomography) scans and fMRI (functional Magnetic Resonance Imaging) scientists have been able to view living, healthy brains. These scans show which areas of the brain are active when a person engages in a specific task, such as learning a new skill,[4] recognizing and comprehending words,[5] and making a decision that involves evaluating risk.[6, 7]

The Plastic Brain

Growing up, most of us were taught that the brain cells we have at birth are all that we'll ever have. The idea was that you could lose brain cells (through damage, disease, alcohol abuse, and the like) but you couldn't grow new ones. This view made it seem like mental strength was something that you were born with but couldn't do much to improve. And it seemed to justify the old saying that "you couldn't teach an old dog new tricks."

Using fMRI and PET scans, however, scientists have been able to view the formation of new brain cells in adult brains and see these new cells become fully integrated into the brain's communication networks.[8]

These findings are exciting because they mean that through nutrition and exercise, you can facilitate the growth of new brain cells. And, more importantly, through brain training, you can rewire your brain to be more efficient at the tasks you want to excel at.

Malleable Minds

Let's look at the evidence of brain plasticity—that is, the brain's malleability—emerging from research today. As John Medina, director of the Brain Center for Applied Learning Research at Seattle Pacific University says:

> "The brain is like a muscle. The more activity you do, the more experience you have, the larger and more complex the brain becomes. Eric Kandel won the Nobel Prize for showing that when people learn something it's because the wiring of their brains changes. You can test sea slugs or human beings, and you will come up with the same results—any creature that ends up learning something does so because of physical changes in its neural architecture.
>
> "This is astonishing. We used to think that we were born with all the neurons we were ever going to get and that it would be hard, if not impossible, to change them beyond a certain age. But it's been quite clear for a while now that the physical changes neurons undergo when learning something happen to anybody's brain at any age. The brain remains quite plastic until we die. We are lifelong learners. That's excellent news indeed."[9]

Numerous other studies have documented how malleable and adaptable adult brains are. A 2007 study of a stroke patient found that her brain had adapted to the damage to the nerves controlling visual information by pulling similar information from other nerves. Similarly, brains of blind people show that the areas of their brain typically used for processing visual information have shifted to verbal processing instead.[10] Numerous other studies have established that neurons reorganize to compensate for damage. Healthy neurons take over for the loss of other nearby neurons.[11]

Boosting the Brain

But what about healthy adult brains? It turns out that healthy brains also rewire based on how they are used. For example, in 1995, a team of scientists used brain-imaging studies of string musicians to show that

the part of the cortex that receives input from the fingers of the left hand was enlarged in those who constantly use the fingers of their left hand when playing their instruments.

In another clever test, a German research team performed a study showing that people who learned how to juggle increased their brain size.[12] The German researchers took 24 non-jugglers and divided them into two groups. One group was asked to do nothing while the other group was asked to practice juggling for three months. Researchers took brain scans of both groups before and after the three-month experiment. Results showed that the group that learned to juggle had increased the volume of their brains. Researchers discovered that the brain developed extra brain cells in the area that is responsible for visual processing and motor skills. Interestingly, when the newly trained jugglers stopped practicing for three months, the parts of their brains that previously increased in size decreased again. Like muscles, brains need to be stimulated and engaged to stay at peak performance.

Training for Intelligence

So far, we've looked at studies proving that the adult brain changes in response to damage, and in response to high-demand needs, such as processing hand-eye coordination. But what about straightforward intelligence? Can you train your brain to be more intelligent? Research by John Jonides and colleagues is showing that you can.

Fluid Intelligence: "Brain Processing Speed"

Scientists have historically believed that fluid intelligence—that is, brain processing ability, not the facts you know—is fixed and is inherited or established very early in life. New research, however, shows that fluid intelligence is 50 to 80 percent inherited, but the rest is influenceable.

Jonides and his colleagues have been experimenting with cognitive training exercises, and they have documented remarkable positive results. In particular, Jonides has focused on training individuals' working memory. Working memory, also known as short-term memory, keeps information at the ready so that you can use it, such as keeping numbers in mind while you add them in your head. Working memory is limited to about five to seven items. For example, a seven-digit phone number is about the limit for most people. You might use the strategy of repeating a phone number to yourself aloud until you're able to make the call. You can think of working memory as being your brain's "desktop"—the more you can keep on the desk for instant access and comparison, the better.

Studies have shown that working memory is responsible for at least 25 percent of the variation in fluid intelligence among individuals. Jonides' research confirms that improving working memory can lead to higher scores on fluid intelligence tests, and this improvement is true for adults, not just children.[13]

Training Working Memory Improves Intelligence

Taking it a step further, Jonides decided to conduct brain training exercises in his lab. He divided individuals randomly into five groups—a control group and four other groups that each got 1, 2, 3, or 4 weeks of brain training depending on their group's number. The training focused on improving their working memory. Jonides' results showed that all groups except the untrained group showed higher scores on the intelligence test after training. Those who had more weeks of training showed more gains, and the four-week training group had the biggest gains. Jonides conducted these tests with young adults as well as with adults over 65 and got the same results.[14]

In a completely separate but related study, researcher Lars Backman showed that test subjects, in this case Finnish men, who underwent working memory training had a higher release of the brain chemical dopamine in the region of the brain important for learning and memory. The before-training and after-training PET scans showed significant increases in dopamine, which is important for learning and memory functions. "These findings suggest that the training improved working memory generally," said Professor Lars Nyberg of Umea University, one of four participating universities in the study.[15]

In short, fMRI scans of blood flow activity and PET scans of chemical activity show that training working memory primed the brain to be better at a multitude of tasks by increasing brain fitness. Furthermore, research on 2,802 senior citizens showed that regular brain training in areas like "processing speed" resulted in improvements that lasted at least five years.[16]

All these results support self-directed neuroplasticity—the ability of individuals to alter their own brain activity through the active practice of focusing attention in constructive ways. Just like Kobe Bryant can boost his physical performance with the right workout regime, you can boost your mental performance with the right workout regime, too. To start, let's look at the role nutrition and physical exercise play in fortifying your brain for optimal performance.

NUTRITION: FEEDING YOUR MENTAL MACHINE

Although your brain only has 2 percent of your body weight, it consumes 20 percent of the oxygen that you breathe and 20 percent of your daily calories. That means that pound-for-pound, your brain uses 10 times the fuel as the other tissues and organs of your body.

Olympians know the importance of nutrition on overall performance. Three-time Olympic gold medal winner in beach volleyball Misty May-Treanor offers advice applicable to executives as well as to athletes: "You learn over time that diet makes a difference in how you perform and compete. You learn what foods provide more energy and strength, and when and what quantities to eat."

Similarly, JC Chamberlain—who plans to set the world record for one hour of cycling despite being over 50—started tracking his food intake a few years ago. He calls it conducting a "personal science project" on himself by testing his food, sleep, exercise, and stress management to see what works best for him.[17]

Eat Right to Think Right

Just as athletes need to eat the right foods to build muscle for strength and have energy for explosive speed or endurance, you, too, need to feed your brain nutrients to keep it functioning optimally.

First, although this book is not about dieting, I must stress one of the things I discovered. Research by UCLA and the University of Pittsburgh found that obese people have smaller brains than peers of their same age group who are not overweight. The researchers measured 94 brains and found that the worst-hit brain areas were those most vital to higher-order reasoning, judgment, and decision-making.[18]

The good news is that losing weight helps reverse the damage done. For example, researchers at the University of Turku in Finland scanned the brains of healthy and obese subjects. Researchers then put the obese subjects on a very low-calorie diet for six weeks and did brain scans again. The scans showed that weight loss reversed the negative effects of obesity on the brain.[19]

The other piece of good news is that foods that are good for your brain are good for your body, so you get a double win when choosing brain-enhancing foods. In fact, it's not just a double win of health and brain power, but more like a home run because of the increased energy and elevated mood that also come from healthy brain functioning.

Water and Electrolytes

The easiest first step to follow is to drink plenty of water. Why? Because the brain is composed of 75 to 80 percent water, which means that dehydration can affect proper brain functioning. Thousands of neuro-chemicals float in the aqueous liquid that protects the brain. Cerebro-spinal fluid is derived from blood plasma and is more than 90 percent water.[20] This fluid is shock absorbing, and it bathes the brain externally. You've likely heard that you need to drink 8 to 10 glasses of water a day, but you may not have realized that it's imperative to keeping your brain adequately hydrated.

Water will also increase your attention because the brain is much more effective when it is well-hydrated. Water makes dopamine (a neu-rotransmitter in the brain) more abundant and more easily received by its receptors. It also enhances neurogenesis (the creation of new brain cells) because new cells need water to survive. Finally, water continu-ally flushes your digestive system, moving food particles along at a rapid rate, which leads to weight loss.

Brains (and muscles) also depend on electrolytes, such as sodium and potassium. The electrical activity of the brain comes from the flow of sodium and potassium ions across the membranes on neurons. That implies that a healthy brain and body need the right balance of these electrolytes. Although most people get more than enough sodium in their modern-day diets, they may not get enough potassium. Potassium-rich foods, such as bananas, also have a positive effect on mood and memory by boosting the neurotransmitter dopamine.

Coffee and Tea

Experts debate the pros and cons of caffeine consumption, and there's no clear consensus yet. In terms of brain functioning, caffeine heightens awareness, but it is not good for deep thought. It stimulates the central nervous system and gets blood pumping to the brain, but it's detrimental if you consume it in too high of doses. Regular caffeine consumption has a positive effect on memory storage and retrieval performance, and it also enhances delayed recall both over the short-term and the long-term.[21] But, too much caffeine (over 300 milligrams per day) may increase your risk of hypertension and coronary disease.[22]

I've been intentionally using the word "caffeine" and not "coffee," which people often automatically equate with caffeine. In fact, many teas also contain caffeine and may even be better sources because they contain more of certain other useful nutrients—namely more antioxidants—than coffee does.

Green, white, and black teas all contain a substance called L-theanine, which stimulates alpha waves. Alpha waves are associated with a relaxed but alert mental state that may also increase attention span. Green tea in particular increases metabolism, decreases appetite, and is linked to preventing many diseases associated with cognitive decline, including heart disease, diabetes, and cancer.

The "Right-Fat" Diet

As stated before, water makes up over 75 percent of the brain. After that, two-thirds of the remainder is made up of fat. Brain cells depend on fat for construction, repair, and ongoing communications in the brain. Dietary fats are critical components of the outer walls of brain cells and the insulating layers that form around nerves, allowing fast transmission of signals back and forth from the brain to the outer reaches of the body.

I say "dietary fats" because the brain needs some kinds of fats that the body can't synthesize. These are omega-3 and omega-6 fatty acids, which must come from your diet. In fact, 20 percent of the dry weight of the brain consists of one particular omega-3 fatty acid, docosahexaenoic acid, or DHA.

Getting enough omega-6 is not difficult in the average American diet because omega-6s are prevalent in chicken, beef, pork, and oils like soybean, safflower, and corn oil. Getting enough omega-3s, on the other hand, is a challenge because omega-3s are found only in a few plants and some seafood.

Yet, the brain needs a ratio of 4:1 of omega-3s to omega-6s. Worse, an excess of omega-6s causes heart disease, vascular disease, and stroke. The highly saturated fats of red meats and dairy can harm the body and the brain. In fact, Dr. Donald Hensrud, a specialist in preventive medicine and nutrition with the Mayo Clinic says, "When blood samples are analyzed after people eat heavy meals, they almost look creamy, and the fat in this blood may displace oxygen."[23]

To get omega-3s, look for cold-water fish such as salmon, sardines, herring, anchovies, tuna, and mackerel. Flaxseeds, walnuts, and walnut oil are also good sources of omega-3s. Given the difficulty of getting enough omega-3s, some chicken farmers are feeding their chickens a flaxseed diet, thereby introducing omega-3s naturally into eggs. Look for these specially marked omega-3 eggs whenever possible. The notion of eggs raising blood cholesterol was disproven years ago. Eggs do not raise cholesterol more than two percent, and they beneficially raise levels of an important chemical, acetylcholine, so feel free to eat eggs daily.

Foods for Brain Speed and Improved Memory

Specifically, to boost brain speed and improve memory, choose foods that contain more acetylcholine. The chemical acetylcholine is a neurotransmitter that determines your brain's processing speed. This brain chemical family also acts as a lubricant and is necessary to keep the internal structures of the body moist so that energy and information can easily pass through each system.[24] When your acetylcholine levels are high, you feel creative, but low acetylcholine significantly decreases brain speed, resulting in "brain fog" and "clouded thinking" which is what you experience when your thinking becomes disjointed.[25]

Fat is a main source of choline. Foods high in choline include almonds, beef (beef liver is especially high), broccoli, cabbage, egg with yolk, fish, peanuts, and peanut butter. Wheat germ is another especially rich source of choline.

Again, the importance of omega-3 fats compared to bad fats plays a key role because bad fats clog your brain and circumvent its production of acetylcholine. Lecithin is a nutrient that your body can use to synthesize choline. If your diet is healthy and balanced, then your liver will produce enough lecithin on its own. If not, eating an eight-ounce serving of some of the above foods once a week is a reasonable supplement.

Foods high in calcium also boost acetylcholine, so choose the following foods to support acetylcholine production and thereby support memory: low-fat milk, cheese, and yogurt as well as nondairy foods like hazelnuts, brazil nuts, blueberries, collard greens, sardines, soy milk, nuts, spinach, and tofu. Low-fat Greek-style yogurt is better than regular yogurt because it contains more protein.

Top 5 Brain-Boosting Snacks

- Handful of raw unsalted nuts
- 1 to 2 hard-boiled eggs
- ½-cup hummus and raw carrots
- 8-oz unflavored low fat Greek yogurt with fresh fruit
- 8-oz yogurt smoothie of fresh fruit, ice, and whey protein

Cinnamon and Spice

Cinnamon has been shown to improve blood-sugar regulation, which can make your mood more stable. And this aromatic spice also boosts brain activity. Research suggests that just smelling cinnamon can enhance brain function. That may be why cinnamon has been shown to improve scores on tests related to attention, memory, and visual-motor speed.[26]

You may have heard about the benefits of other foods and nutrients, too. The ones named here are by no means a comprehensive list. Plus, researchers are continuing to discover more and more about the effect of foods on our brain functioning. The key message: What you eat and drink is critical to keeping your brain in shape.

EXERCISE: HEALTHY BODY, HEALTHY BRAIN

Regular exercise goes hand-in-hand with nutrition to achieve a healthy body primed for optimal performance. That's a fact we've all known for a long time. What hasn't been known until recently is the beneficial effects of exercise on the brain. Here I'm talking not just about doing crossword puzzles, sudoku, or other such brain exercises. Rather, I'm talking about regular physical exercise like running, biking, swimming, basketball, and working out. Aerobic exercise as well as resistance exercise, or strength training, benefits the brain in documented, measurable ways. Simply put, exercise changes your brain chemistry, promoting the ability of the brain to remain flexible and rewire itself.[27]

Muscle Fuel Is Also Brain Fuel

Scientific research shows that regular exercise, even walking, leads to more robust mental abilities, and this is true throughout the lifespan from childhood to old age. How does it work? Regular exercise increases glycogen storage in muscles as well as in the brain, where it helps to fuel neurons. Remember that your brain needs lots of energy—it burns 20 percent of your daily calories. Research has shown that the gains from exercise were most dramatic in brain areas critical to learning and memory.[28]

Healthy Heart, Healthy Brain

Why is exercise beneficial for brain functioning? Exercise is good for the cardiovascular system—your heart and arteries. The brain has lots of blood vessels, just like the rest of the body, so that means that exercise will help keep the brain's blood vessels healthy, too. And there's an added benefit: preventing Alzheimer's disease. The majority of Alzheimer's cases are due to restricted blood flow, not genetic factors. Vascular problems lead to micro-strokes in the brain, which damage the brain the same way that genetic Alzheimer's does. By improving your cardiovascular system through aerobic exercise, you reduce these micro-strokes and the likelihood of Alzheimer's. People who exercise are 50 percent less likely to get the disease.[29]

Athletic Bodies, Faster Minds

Furthermore, a study reported in the *Journal of American College of Sports Medicine* found that people who were athletic seemed to have better focus and faster processing speed than nonathletes. This faster processing is likely due to the demand for rapid evaluations and decision making required in complex environments.

Participants in the study consisted of 36 male and female students, ages 18 to 22. Half of the participants were varsity athletes representing a wide variety of sports including cross-country running, baseball, swimming, tennis, wrestling, soccer, and gymnastics. Some participants were chosen for their notable endurance, some for strength and power, and others for precision and grace. The remaining participants were not athletes but were young collegians from a variety of academic departments.

In the study, scientists examined whether being proficient at sports would translate into success at real-world everyday tasks. Participants were asked to complete a series of virtual-reality tasks of navigating through traffic without getting hit. Results showed that the student athletes navigated better than the nonathletes, although their success was not a result of their being quicker or more athletic. Their success was a result of their enhanced ability to gather more data in the situation and process it faster and more accurately than the other students.[30]

The Value of Aerobic Exercise

Aerobic exercise also improves your reaction time and overall attention. In a multifaceted test conducted by the University of Illinois, students were asked to memorize a string of letters and then pick out those letters from a list that was flashed at them. Next, the students were divided randomly into three groups. One group was asked to sit quietly for the next 30 minutes. The second group had to run on a treadmill for 30 minutes, and the final group lifted weights for 30 minutes. Then all groups were tested again, having to pick out the previously memorized letters from lists flashed at them, just like before. This time, however, the students who had run for 30 minutes were noticeably quicker than either

the weight-lifting or the resting group. Finally, all groups were given another 30-minute rest period and were tested again. As before, the group that had run for 30 minutes continued to outperform the weight-lifting group and the resting group.

Another study compared the effects of six months of light aerobic exercise (brisk walking) versus six months of flexibility training in a group of elderly people. Those who had walked regularly showed notable improvements in their mental test scores. Those who had flexibility training showed improved physical flexibility but not cognitive improvements. [31]

Findings such as these have led neuroscientists like Peter Snyder to say that exercise is the best memory enhancer. Running and other forms of aerobic exercise have been shown to create new brain cells in the parts of the brain associated with memory and thinking.

Muscle Growth Stimulates Brain Growth

Although aerobic exercise is superior to muscle-building training when it comes to a direct link with cognitive performance and improvements, building muscle mass does have a positive benefit on the brain. A study at the Department of Molecular Neurobiology at the University of Groningen showed that building muscle mass leads to both neurogenesis, which is the creation of new brain cells, and angiogenesis, which is the increase in the amount of blood that flows to the brain.[32]

Another study from the Brain Research Center at the University of British Columbia showed that older women who lifted weights performed significantly better on various tests of cognitive functioning than women who completed toning or stretching classes.[33]

Recent research by evolutionary biologists and anthropologists has shown that there's a deep, evolutionary basis for the relationship between a healthy body and a healthy mind, according to Harvard evolutionary biologist Daniel E. Lieberman. Here's how researchers figured it out: First, they bred mice and rats to be marathon runners. That is, they took the animals that by choice ran the longest on exercise wheels and bred them with each other, leading to rodents that excelled at running. The scientists then studied the animals over generations and found that the marathon animals began to develop inherently high levels of substances that promote brain tissue growth and health, including a protein called brain-derived neurotrophic factor (BDNF).[34] These substances are important for endurance performance—and they are known to drive brain growth. It follows, then, that if physical activity helped to mold the structure of our brains, it most likely remains essential to brain health today, asserts John D. Polk, an associate professor of anthropology at the University of Illinois at Urbana-Champaign.[35]

Go Aerobic

The recommendations from all this research point to active aerobic exercise on a regular basis, with some strength training added in as well. When choosing among different kinds of aerobic exercise, you'll benefit your brain even more by choosing a competitive sport or physical activity that involves movements that you're not able to anticipate. For example, basketball, tennis, soccer, and even ping-pong are better than golf or swimming, where the movements are much more predictable as opposed to requiring fast reaction. This is even true if you're playing Wii games—Wii Tennis is better than Wii Golf, even though neither are very aerobic. Reacting quickly to unexpected moves gives your brain an added workout.

What's more, exercise improves your ability to handle uncertainty and stress. Exercise not only reduces muscle tension, which thereby reduces the feeling of anxiety, but it also increases levels of the neurotransmitters serotonin and gamma-aminobutryric acid (GABA) in your brain, which lowers anxiety and increases your memory capacity.[36]

Get Some Sun

If you have the chance, exercise outside or at least take some time to be outside during periods of sunshine. Sunshine helps elevate levels of vitamin D, and research suggests that adequate amounts may play a role in sustaining energy. For no particularly good reason, I've always scheduled my own routine physicals in the winter and very often my doctor tells me my vitamin D level is low. Without enough sun in the winter, supplements are in order. Experts suspect vitamin D helps regulate metabolism and insulin secretion, both of which have an impact on energy. The sunlight will also help maintain your circadian rhythm for more energetic days and more restful nights.

Working Harder Vs. Working Smarter

For those who think that they don't have time to exercise, or who think that they're too tired to exercise, consider that regular exercise increases energy levels by 20 percent.[37] Furthermore, not taking time to exercise and eat right can actually backfire. Rather than saving time, it leads to poorer, slower, less innovative, and shallower creative output, says serial entrepreneur and former hedge-fund lawyer Jonathan Fields. Fields has often heard entrepreneurs give (and has himself given) excuses like, "I'm launching a damn company and my hair's on fire. I don't have time to work out" only to miss the productivity boost and elevated mood and cognitive function that physical exercise brings.[38] Making 80 hours per week of poor judgments is no way to run a business.

Finally, researchers have found a strong correlation between effective leadership and regular exercise. For example, coworkers give higher leadership effectiveness ratings to executives who exercise.[39] Exercisers score higher than non-exercisers in all leadership categories, including credibility, leading others, and authenticity. Despite these findings, less than half of executives surveyed said they themselves are role models for diet, health, and fitness. Results were no better for colleagues: When asked about other senior leaders in their organizations, just 33 percent said their colleagues were role models of healthfulness.

Given the findings, it's clear that keeping a healthy body is key to keeping a healthy mind. To be a more effective, efficient leader, you not only need to pay attention to what you put into your body, but also how you exercise it.

5

SLEEP: THE UNDERVALUED RESOURCE

Although we usually measure our brain's performance by what it does during the day, what it does at night may be just as important. Sleep seems to be the time that your brain does its "back-office paperwork"— filing away the day's experiences into long-term memory and making new connections. Although sleep seems like wasted "downtime," it's actually an active process vital for mental performance.

Sleeping for Success

The parents of a figure skater came to Dr. James Maas, author of *Sleep for Success*.[40] Their daughter was good and she was trying to improve, training twice a day—first early in the morning and then later in the afternoon. Dr. Maas advised eliminating the daughter's morning practice, thereby giving her an extra hour of sleep from seven hours to eight. Soon after the change, her grades rose and she became physically stronger in her skating. "Sleeping builds muscle and enhances athletic performance," Dr. Maas said. The daughter was Sarah Hughes who went on to the Olympics and won the gold medal in figure skating.

Athletes have instinctively known the importance of sleep in achieving good athletic performance. Only in recent years, however, have researchers systematically documented the results that good sleep brings. What's more, the improvements are not only in physical ability but mental performance as well.

Boarding Schools Get on Board

Deerfield Academy in Massachusetts invited Dr. Maas to speak and then implemented some of his suggestions. Specifically, the school delayed class start time to 8:30 a.m. from the original 7:55 a.m. They also shortened sports practices and homework loads by 10 percent each and required students to be back in their dorms earlier at night. The results showed a record increase in GPA among students, better rankings among the school's sports teams across several disciplines, and 20 percent fewer student visits to the health center, despite it being a bad flu year.

Sleep Improves Performance

When the Stanford Men's Basketball team was asked to participate in a sleep study, the team already exhibited impressive performance. Athletes reported sleeping eight hours a night and being in peak physical condition. Nonetheless, they agreed to participate in the study. [41]

During the first 2 to 4 weeks, the players were asked to do what they normally do, just with the addition of wearing wristbands that monitored their sleep. During the second 5 to 7 weeks, players were asked to get 10 hours of sleep a night, including naps during the day if they weren't able to get 10 hours during the night.

The players were tested after the first period of regular sleep and again at the end of the period of longer sleep. The results—even among these elite athletes in peak condition—were dramatic. With no other change to their routines than the added sleep, the players ran faster on timed sprints, and their shooting accuracy on free throws and three-point shots improved 9 percent. [42] What's more, all 11 players got these improvements and all reported improved performance during competitive basketball games. As sleep researcher Cheri Mah said, it's not that the athletes weren't already functioning well, but the added sleep improved their performance.

There's another lesson to be learned from this study. Interestingly, even though athletes reported regularly sleeping 8 hours a night during their pre-test, the wristbands showed that they only slept 6 hours and 45 minutes a night. When asked to sleep 10 hours a night, they in fact only slept 8.5. So the time period that you're sleeping may not in fact be the actual amount of sleep you're getting. When you allot more time to sleep, you increase the chances of actually getting the amount of sleep you need. In the case of the athletes, that additional 90 minutes brought them their dramatic gains in speed and accuracy.

Sleep Deprivation Hurts the Body and Mind

If you've been up for 21 hours, that's the equivalent of being legally drunk, according to Sean Drummond of UC-San Diego. Former President Bill Clinton said that every mistake he ever made was when he was tired. Some hard-charging industries like investment banking—not to mention start-up entrepreneurs—make pulling all-nighters a point of pride and part of getting ahead. But a lack of sleep takes its toll. A 2012 University of Southern California study of young investment bankers found that sleep deprivation contributed to physical and emotional ailments within four years on the job.

"People in investment banking have been my main clients for the last few years because they're so exhausted and under so much pressure," said Dr. Maas in an article in *The Wall Street Journal*.[43]

Debunking the Myth of Sleep Deprivation

After some rocky years in high school, and being lucky to get into a college at all, university gave me a fresh start. One of the things that helped me do quite well is counterintuitive to most college students: relaxing and sleeping before a test. I would start studying for tests much earlier than my classmates, often just 20 minutes at a time but as much as a week before a test. So while most other students I went to school with "crammed" the night before a test, often until the wee hours of the morning, I made a habit of going out with friends and getting to bed reasonably early. In fact, I developed a reputation for being the one who could go out, not worry about the test, and still do well. The reputation felt good and probably reinforced the behavior. And the importance of sleep stuck with me as I went into the Navy.

After graduating college, I joined the U.S. Navy's Nuclear Submarine program, starting out in the Navy's Officer Candidate School (OCS). After earning my commission at OCS, I spent the next 18 months in various schools, learning the principles of nuclear power, and how to actually operate a live nuclear power plant and submarine systems. I then reported to a submarine—the USS Norfolk, a Los Angeles-class attack submarine.

When an officer first reports to a submarine, he is considered useless by the rest of the officers on board. Despite all of the training, it takes many months before becoming qualified on that submarine—first to run the engine room, which is a nuclear power plant, and finally to run the entire ship. While every ship has a captain, an "officer of the deck" is in charge of operating the ship, typically for a 6-hour shift.

The life of a new officer can, in many respects, be compared to that of new medical interns and residents. The hours are grueling and sleep deprivation is the norm. A new officer is expected to spend every free minute studying and working on the qualification in order to take on his or her own shifts, thus relieving the workload on the other officers.

Well, again, I decided sleep was important. So while most officers were accustomed to 18- to 20-hour days, running themselves down to the point of being walking zombies, I went to sleep. I'd be lying if I said I consistently got 8 hours of sleep; 6 was a victory. But I certainly got more than anyone else—and at a great price. I was kicked at times (my bunk was on the bottom) and awakened in many different ways, all because of the perception of my future peers that I was lazy. Nonetheless, I stayed the course.

Months later, it turns out I qualified to drive that ship as officer of the deck faster than anyone else ever had. The tone of everyone I worked with quickly changed. People started valuing their sleep more. And a minor culture change was underway. No one ever bothered me about how much I slept again because they came to realize that when I was awake, I got more done than anyone else. In fact there were quite a few times that I would swap shifts and cover for someone who was getting run down so they could catch up on their sleep.

In today's fast-paced world, operating on less sleep has almost become a badge of honor for some. I hear executives say to one another all the time, "I only need 6 hours of sleep a night," and another might counter with, "I generally get about 5." It's a competition of sorts, the belief being that the less sleep you get, the harder you must work, but nothing could be further from the truth.

Are You Getting Enough Sleep?

To gauge if you're getting enough sleep, ask yourself:

1) Do you remember your dreams? If so, that's a sign that you are getting good sleep.
2) Do you need an alarm to get you up in the morning, or can you wake up without one? If you can wake up without an alarm, that suggests you're well-rested.

How Many Hours of Sleep Do You Need?

Do some self-diagnostics to see how many hours are right for you. Eight hours a night is average; it's rare for people to function well on 4 hours. Learn what's optimal for you. On days that you miss getting enough sleep, go to bed early rather than waking up late the next day, so that you maintain a consistent wake-up time.

While You Sleep, Your Brain Works

Sleep is crucial for learning, remembering, and executing complex tasks. According to neurological researcher Paul Bendheim, there is increasingly solid evidence that sleep enhances learning and problem-solving in an active way, not just a passive way. While you sleep, the hippocampus and the cortical networks of memory and learning are activated repeatedly. The same brain cells used during the day—whether studying Spanish, trying out a new computer, or memorizing the member states of the EU—are now repeating the same patterns of firing while you sleep. During these sleep "rehearsals," temporary memories of important learned skills and facts are transferred to long-term memory for storage and recall on demand.[44]

These rehearsals are truly rehearsals. A Belgian study found that the identical pattern of brain activity that test subjects displayed while learning a computer task was repeated exactly the same during sleep.[45] The brain literally repeats and practices the newly learned task while you sleep, strengthening the synaptic connections between cells to solidify the memory and skills. So don't think of your sleep time as lost time—it's rehearsal time to cement what you know.

Sleep and Creativity

Sleep isn't just critical for learning. Sleep is also vital for creative breakthroughs. Tales are often told of breakthrough ideas coming to people in their sleep or dreams. Although many of these stories leave out all the prior hard work and thinking that went into the endeavor

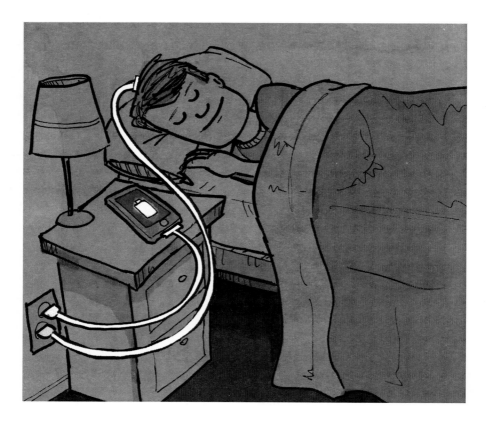

before the dream, it is true that sleep played a role in getting the insight. Research from Harvard Medical School and from Germany bears this out. For example, the German study asked adults to perform a challenging math task. The math task could be solved—and be solved more quickly—if the individual grasped a hidden shortcut. Participants were given some initial training on the math task. Then, half the participants were allowed a good night's sleep while the other participants were not.

Eight hours later, all participants were asked to solve the math task. Participants who had gotten the good night's sleep were almost three times as likely to discover the hidden shortcut compared to participants who were sleep-deprived. The sleep-deprived participants lumbered their way through the task through repetition, but those who had slept solved it by getting the insight. They got the insight because during sleep, the hippocampus processed the learning and knowledge that the participants had gained during their training on the task. During sleep, the structuring and reordering of these memory elements made the participants much more likely to hit upon the insight.[46]

Similarly, psychologist Deirdre Barrett at Harvard Medical School's Behavioral Medicine Program researched creative problem-solving and found that those "Aha!" moments during dreams almost always occurred after the individual had worked on the problem extensively during waking hours.[47] Sleep lets the brain continue processing the daytime work to solve the stumbling block. The solution came by accessing other related memories that were suppressed during active wakeful work as "irrelevant" to the task but were actually relevant in an unexpected way. Sleep allowed these related but seemingly irrelevant memories to be activated, and the dreamer recognized their relevance to the solution upon awakening.

How to Get a Good Night's Sleep

Given the importance of sleep, how do you get a good night's rest? It's not easy. In fact, the Centers for Disease Control and Prevention estimate that 40.6 million American workers—30 percent of the workforce—get less than 6 hours of sleep a night, which means they aren't sleeping enough to function at peak levels. Researchers at Harvard Medical School estimated in 2011 that sleep deprivation cost American companies $63.2 billion a year in lost productivity. The phenomenon is called "presenteeism"—showing up for work but functioning at second-rate levels.

Sleep Facts

"It takes one hour of sleep to pay for every two hours of wakefulness."
   – James Maas, author of *Sleep for Success*[48]

There's a significant link between a lack of sleep and stress, depression, ability to think and perform, hypertension, heart attacks, strokes, Type 2 diabetes, periodontal disease, skin problems, obesity, and cancer.[49]

Companies like Procter & Gamble, as well as hospitals, healthcare, and finance companies are hiring sleep experts to design sleep courses for their employees. Here are some tips courses like these offer:

1) **Have a pre-bedtime ritual that you follow every night.** This cues your body that it's time for sleep. The ritual can include brushing your teeth, having a soothing cup of hot chamomile tea, turning down the bed, or perhaps doing some easy reading.

2) **Go to bed at about the same time each night and wake up at about the same time each morning.** The consistency helps your circadian rhythm and sleep cycle.

3) **Keep a notepad next to your bed.** If your mind starts to race with to-dos that lay ahead, write them down. That way, you don't have to keep thinking about them, because they'll be on your notepad in the morning.

4) **Stay hydrated.** Dehydration can also impact sleep, so that's another reason to stay hydrated. Keep this in mind when traveling because long flights add to dehydration.

5) **Use earplugs and sleep shades.** This ensures a dark, quiet sleep environment.

6) **Turn down the thermostat.** The body's natural body temperature lowers in preparation for sleep so by turning down the thermostat you're helping to stimulate that natural phenomenon.

7) **Avoid TV and computers or mobile devices an hour before bed.** These devices emit blue light, the light present in sunlight, which makes your body think it's daytime and interferes with your body's ability to produce melatonin, a natural sleep hormone. Therefore, it's not just the activity of texting or emailing that keeps your mind racing, but also the blue light from the screen that contributes to wakefulness as well.

8) **Monitor your sleep.** Several tools and apps are available that can help you track data about how many hours you're sleeping and the quality of your sleep.

More Sleep Leads to Podium Finish

Scott Dunlap, an elite-level marathon runner, began incorporating sleep into his training in about 2009. "If you look at my training plan, sleep is right there along with mileage and pace," said Dunlap, now 44. Dunlap gets about 6 or 7 hours of sleep during a regular training cycle, but he increases that to 9 or 10 hours in the two weeks before a big race. "Once I started tracking my sleep, I realized I wasn't getting nearly enough," Dunlap said. "My performance picked up dramatically when I slept more. It was the difference between finishing barely in the top 10 and finishing on the podium.[50]

6

STRESS: THE CREATIVITY KILLER

Stress is part of everyday life, especially if you want to push the limits of performance, get out of your comfort zone, and take competitive risks needed for success. But prolonged, unrelenting stress is bad for your body and can damage your brain. Under stress, the body produces glucocorticoids—hormones that are useful for short-term response to trauma but that can cause damage over the long-term. Operating at the highest levels of performance means managing stress.

Excessive Anxiety: Toxic to the Mind

Stress hormones hit the hippocampus, which plays an important role in learning and memory. Over time, the glucocorticoid loop damages the hippocampus. Developmental molecular biologist and brain expert John J. Medina has found that stressed people don't do math very well, don't process language efficiently, and have poorer memories, both short-term and long-term.[51]

Too much stress also disturbs your ability to concentrate, because it arouses the amygdala, seat of your fear response. Stress impairs your prefrontal cortex and working memory, hindering your decision-making prowess.[52]

Even worse in these complex times, the brain under stress favors rigid *habit* memory over more flexible *cognitive* memory. That is, under times of stress, the brain reverts to stimulus-response behavior, taking action based on habitual associations rather than a more adaptive learning strategy.[53] This is particularly bad news when we need creativity and imagination to help us respond innovatively to competitive threats and uncertain markets.

How to Conquer Stress

How can you overcome stress? The most effective way to manage stress—physical exercise—is also demonstrably beneficial to the brain. Cardiologists Richard Milani and Carl Lavie, who have written more than 70 papers on the effect of exercise on the heart, have also written 11 papers focused on the effect of exercise on anxiety. Exercise "has been shown to lead to reductions of more than 50 percent in the prevalence of the symptoms of anxiety. This supports exercise training as an additional method to reduce chronic anxiety."[54]

Similarly, a 2004 study at the University of Southern Mississippi had students walk at 50 percent of their maximum heart rate or run on treadmills at 60 to 90 percent of their maximum heart rate. Both groups reduced their sensitivity to anxiety, with the high-intensity exercise group getting the most benefit. Even better, these benefits began after just the second exercise session.

Dr. John Ratey, associate clinical professor of psychiatry at Harvard Medical School, explains these findings through biology. As we saw in the exercise chapter, exercise affects the chemistry mix in the brain. Exercise also changes the way we process fear and anxiety, just as endorphins reduce the experience of pain.[55]

Herbal Teas Tame Tension

I didn't mention herbal teas in the nutrition chapter because herbal teas are not teas at all, and they don't contain the L-theanine found in actual tea leaves. But, herbal teas do play a useful role in calming a stressed, racing brain. Chamomile, lemon balm, and passionflower herbal teas, in particular, are all good at reducing stress and taming tension.

The aroma of that calming cup can also be part of healthy habits for getting a good night's sleep. The scent of the herbal tea tells the brain that it's time to switch gears, calm down, and prepare for the night-shift of mental activities of REM sleep.

Supersonic Skydiver Felix Baumgartner

Former military parachutist Felix Baumgartner had faced and defeated fear more than 2,500 times—that's how many jumps he'd made before announcing his plan to skydive from 120,000 feet above the earth. But his plan to dive from space encountered an unexpected obstacle. Felix would have to wear a space suit and helmet during his dive to prevent getting ebullism (a potentially fatal condition) from spending 5 hours at such high altitude on his way up to the edge of space and then leaping back down.

Felix hadn't worn space suits before—and he instantly disliked them. They restricted his movement, and the helmet's glass fogged up, impairing his visual field. The combination left Felix feeling claustrophobic, to the point that he began having panic attacks. All that's understandable, but not acceptable if your goal is to break a world record. Felix knew he'd have to fight his battle head-on, literally, if he wanted to achieve his dream.

Felix worked with sports psychologist Michael Gervais, a specialist in high-performance and extreme sports, to conquer his unexpected fear. First, Gervais identified the source of Felix's fear. It wasn't so much the suit as what the suit had come to represent to Felix: a symbol of not having complete control of the situation. In previous jumps, Felix knew the capabilities of his body and eyesight. Now, those capabilities might be compromised by the suit. The unease diverted Felix's attention to his suit, Gervais said, and Felix had to get his focus back on his goal. "When we are in a high stakes or intense situation, it's not uncommon for our minds to jump forward, going to the next moment and worrying about what happens when this moment doesn't go well," Gervais said. "What happens is we give 50 percent to something that doesn't exist yet and 50 to this moment."[56]

To get back on track, Felix had to:

- Master combat breathing—deep breathing to calm himself.
- Develop positive self-talk, using great care in choosing the words he'd use when talking to himself and others about the jump.
- Learn to handle increasingly uncomfortable situations to prove he had control over his body and mind.

"We cultivated a situation to move a person to the edge of panic," said Gervais. "Imagine doing that repeatedly over 30 hours of training and at the end of it, you've got full control of how your mind works, and you breathe freely in those moments."

Finally, the flight team devised a detailed prelaunch procedure to help occupy Felix's mind before lift-off.

In the end, Felix conquered his fear and set a world record for skydiving 24 miles at a speed of 843 miles per hour, faster than Mach 1, thereby also becoming the first person to break the sound barrier without vehicular power.

So, as we can learn from Felix, even stress in extreme circumstances can be conquered with the right approach. When we prepare ourselves and build in intentional relaxation, like breathing deep or stepping away from the computer for a walk, we'll be more successful—and healthier—than if we let stress take control.

MENTAL STAMINA

Businesspeople need endurance in these days of global business, which spans multiple time zones and demands early morning and late night meetings on a regular basis. What's more, tight economic times demand greater spans of control, giving managers more teams and projects under their purview.

Mental Stamina Through Physical Stamina

What are some ways to set yourself up for the long run? As you learned in Chapter 4 on Exercise, one of the best ways to prepare is literally to run or to do other regular aerobic exercise to keep our heart and blood pumping comfortably.

Brad Feld, an entrepreneur and venture capitalist for more than 20 years, described the endurance that entrepreneurs need. "Anyone that knows me, or has worked with me, knows that in addition to being able to cover a wide range of things simultaneously, I can also go very deep on one thing for a long period of time. It's this second trait that I think is so important for both serious athletes as well as great entrepreneurs."[57] One tactic Feld himself uses is to run marathons. Running has also helped him trim extra pounds that had begun to creep on. And, as a competitive, ever-striving businessman, Feld has made it a goal to run a marathon in all 50 states. He's at 22 of 50 as of this writing.

Mental Stamina Through Task Switching

The second tactic for endurance is to switch tasks. There's a biological basis for mental fatigue that doesn't necessarily mean that your entire brain is too tired for all tasks. Rather, the brain may be overextended on the particular task you've been working on. The concept, as University of Cambridge neuroscientist John Coates explains, is called "metabolic cost." That is, mental fatigue is a signal that the expected return on your current activity has dropped below its metabolic cost. Brains continually search for the optimal way to allocate attention and metabolic results. Fatigue is a signal that you've been activating the same neural pathways too long. You're unlikely to make good progress at the moment if you continue. Your brain is signaling that it's stuck in a rut.[58]

The cure for mental fatigue, Coates advocates, is not a rest but a fresh task. "Support for this idea comes from data showing that overtime work does not in itself lead to work-related illness such as hypertension and heart disease; these occur mainly if workers have no control over the allocation of their attention," Coates says. "Applying such a model could benefit workers and management alike, for more flexibility in choosing what to work on, and when, could reduce worker fatigue."

Coates has found that mental fatigue typically disappears if you switch tasks. That wouldn't happen if you'd exhausted all your brain's capacity. This strategy of switching tasks is particularly important to creativity and imagination.

Long-Distance Thinking

Prize-winning novelist Haruki Murakami maintains a strict schedule of writing, running and swimming, and getting enough sleep when working on his bestselling novels. He runs a 10k or swims 1,500 meters every day when he writes, as a way to "mesmerize myself to reach a deeper state of mind." As he sees it, "writing a long novel is like survival training. Physical strength is as necessary as artistic sensitivity."[59]

When we hear a story such as Murakami's, it's easy to think it's an anomaly, but there are many examples out there of people in all professions who practice specific techniques to increase their mental stamina. You may not need to run six miles a day, but you do need to find ways to beat mental fatigue. Exercise, task switching, and finding your physical strengths are key.

PATTERN RECOGNITION AND EXPERTISE

Malcolm Gladwell popularized the 10,000-hour rule in his book, *Outliers*.[60] The rule says that a person requires 10,000 hours of practice to become an expert in something. For most people, 10,000 hours translates to about 10 years of work in the field. Neurologist David Levitin found that this number held consistently across all manner of fields of

endeavor, from composers to basketball players, fiction writers, ice skaters, concert pianists, chess players, and even master criminals.[61]

Expertise: From Conscious Effort to Ingrained Patterns

Expertise is based on pattern recognition. Elite basketball players can look at the court and quickly anticipate what the team is doing. Chess experts can look at a chess board and recognize a move to make from past patterns of chess boards they've seen—they don't have to laboriously think through all the possible moves one-by-one the way that nonexperts must.

One of the reasons the 10,000-hour rule works is that it describes the length of time it takes to build up repertoires of patterns and have them ingrained enough to be automatic. Making it "automatic" means that the task can be handled by the more primitive parts of the brain, rather than the working-memory-constrained conscious mind. The difference between the novice and the expert is that the novice must think through the solution, which takes time. In contrast, the expert immediately knows the answer because repeated experience has ingrained the pattern.

The most common example is learning to drive a car, which at first takes cognitive effort but with practice becomes automatic, requiring much less conscious thought than initially. Developing expertise works the same way, just over longer time periods given the complexity of becoming an expert compared to simply executing one skill.

fMRI tests prove that experts use different parts of their brains than amateurs do when performing a task in their area of expertise. For example, scientist Xiaohong Wan examined amateurs and professionals of Japanese chess (*shogi*) under an MRI to compare the differences in brain activity when they were presented with various *shogi* board patterns and were told to think of their next move. The MRI results showed that certain brain regions of experts lit up in areas that amateurs' did not. Apparently, the experts were accessing parts of their brain that maximized intuition by utilizing episodic memory with goal-seeking and pattern recognition.[62]

Anders Ericsson, similarly, has been studying experts and expertise for decades. Consistently and overwhelmingly, he has found that experts are made, not born, and that the path to expertise involves deliberate practice. Ericsson appends the adjective "deliberate" because the practice must involve pushing yourself beyond your current comfort and ability.

Not All Practice Makes Perfect

As Ericsson jokingly says, "Living in a cave does not make you a geologist." Not all practice makes perfect. You need a particular kind of practice—deliberate practice—to develop expertise. When most people practice, they focus on the things they already know how to do. Deliberate practice is different. It entails considerable, specific, and sustained efforts to do something you can't do well—or even do at all. Research across domains shows that it is only by working at what you can't do that develops expertise in a domain.[63]

Deliberate practice involves not only improving the skills you have but also extending the reach and range of your skills. You have to put in the hours. Golfer Sam Snead, who's been called "the best natural player ever," told *Golf Digest*, "People always said I had a natural swing. They thought I wasn't a hard worker. But when I was young, I'd play and practice all day, then practice more at night by my car's headlights. My hands bled. Nobody worked harder at golf than I did."

Across all his studies, Ericsson has found no evidence of "naturals" who have floated to the top of their field without extensive practicing. The people at the very top don't just work harder than everyone else—they work much, much harder.[64]

Deliberate Practice in Action: Ben Franklin

A good example of deliberate practice in the intellectual area—in this case writing eloquently and persuasively—is Ben Franklin. When Franklin decided to learn to write persuasively, he began by studying his favorite articles from a popular British publication, *The Spectator*. Days after he'd read an article he particularly enjoyed, he would try to reconstruct it from memory in his own words. Then he would compare it with the original, so he could discover and correct his faults. He also worked to improve his sense of language by translating the articles into rhyming verse and then from verse back into prose. Similarly, famous painters often learn by attempting to reproduce the paintings of other masters.[65]

Gaining Expert Intuition

Pursuing this path of deliberate practice toward expertise hones your intuition. William Duggan of Columbia University describes this "expert intuition" as being based on feeling rather than thinking.[66] Expert intuition is a form of rapid thinking in which you jump to a conclusion based on a pattern you recognize. With expert intuition, the more experienced a person is in a given profession, the quicker and easier it is for them to recognize patterns that have occurred in the past, resulting in faster, more accurate problem solving.[67]

Pattern Recognition Reduces Demands on Working Memory

As described in Chapter 2 on The Brain, working memory puts the biggest limit on your thinking capacity. Being able to hold only about five to seven items at a time in memory is constraining. But, the good news is that this limit can be for chunks of items, not necessarily individual digits. For example, for most Americans, recalling the numbers 1-7-7-6 doesn't require four-item placeholders because "1776" is a number most Americans recognize as the historical founding date of the United States. Thus, "1776" can be stored as a single chunk more easily than "5793" might be.

The process of building expertise is one of building these chunks or patterns. For example, when seeing a bird, an expert birdwatcher doesn't have to say, "Hmm, a long red tail, a yellow beak…" enumerating all the characteristics of the bird to identify it. The bird is recognized at a glance from long practice, just like you can recognize your spouse or parent at one glance.

Quick-Win Working Memory Tip

The items that working memory keeps in mind aren't only numbers or patterns or concepts. Working memory also gets crowded with extraneous thoughts you're having, such as "I'm not good at this task" or "I still have to prepare for next week's speech." Any thoughts that are in your conscious awareness detract from your working memory capacity. This explains why test anxiety leads to worse performance on tests.

Anyone who's taking a test while having thoughts like "I don't know if I'll be able to finish this test on time" is cluttering up their working memory with thoughts that aren't helpful to them actually answering the test questions. Cognitive scientist Sian Beilock has found that simply having anxious students spend 10 minutes writing their thoughts and feelings immediately before taking a test improved their test scores. Writing down the thoughts helped clear them from their minds.[68]

Dismissing distracting thoughts helps you put all the resources of your working memory to work on the task at hand, improving your performance.

9

DECISION-MAKING AND COGNITIVE TRAPS

Besides improving mental acuity, another way to improve the productive results of your brainpower is to be aware of cognitive traps. These traps are errors that result from the way the brain naturally works, so we're rarely aware of them, but they lead us to make wrong decisions. What's worse, we're not aware that we're making wrong decisions. In fact, for cognitive reasons, some very sound decisions may actually feel "wrong." Let's take a look at each of these decision traps so that you can quickly spot them and stop them before they derail you.

Availability Bias and Recency Bias

The first cognitive trap is called availability bias. That is, we tend to think that one thing caused something else or that one thing is more likely to happen than something else simply because it is more easily called up from memory. That is, it's readily "available" and therefore seems more likely or prevalent than it actually is. Another reason for availability or easy recall of something is vividness. That is, if something is more vivid, it is more likely to be recalled from memory, whether it is relevant to the decision or not.

For example, people think that flying in an airplane is more dangerous than driving a car, because they can recall horrific news reports of flaming aircraft crashes. In truth, 40,000 people die in car crashes every year compared to 200 in airplane crashes, but airplane crashes are much more dramatic and vivid, making them easier to recall.[69]

A related cognitive trap is called the recency bias. It's related to availability in that a more recent fact or event is more likely to be recalled. Again, it's more available in memory.

Anchoring Errors

Another cognitive trap, anchoring, is a trap to be especially aware of in negotiations. Anchoring happens when we quickly make some assessment or calculation (usually based on the most salient or available information) and then we tend to make adjustments to that initial position as we get more information, rather than abandoning that initial position.

The initial number or assessment therefore creates an "anchor" which is then adjusted slightly but not drastically. Anchoring can have a profound effect on negotiations if, for example, the opening figure stated for a purchase is high or low. If the initial number stated is $30 per square foot, it may be adjusted to $20 to $40 but not to $145 easily.

Framing Errors

Finally, framing—the way a problem is initially stated—can be another source of error. Consider the statements: "50 percent of patients using this drug are expected to live" compared to "50 percent of patients using this drug are expected to die." Although the two statements define an identical 50:50 outcome, the latter statement rings alarm bells for the negative consequences and thus would be met with more resistance than the former.

Gut Feel

Sometimes there are reasons why we have a "gut feel" about something—and why that gut feel could be wrong. This phenomenon is a tricky one and depends on whether the gut feel is a result of expertise or not. When the gut feel comes as a result of accumulated past experience, it can be right because it's based on a mass of patterns that let you know what to do even if you can't articulate all the reasons. Within your domain of expertise, gut feel can encapsulate more than your conscious mind, with its limited short-term memory, can explain. In the case of expertise, then, "gut feel" decisions can be right because of the thousands of patterns the expert has learned over the years.

The time to be careful and conscious of a gut feel is when you are making a decision either outside of your typical realm or in a new way, such as making a decision that involves following a new strategy. These decisions may feel "wrong" primarily because they are new. Your amygdala, seat of emotion and fear, is programmed to be on the lookout for anything new. Throughout evolutionary history, something new and unfamiliar could be threatening, so human brains are primed to detect it and be on the alert for it.

As a result, you may feel this same sort of unease or discomfort when you make a new decision, but that discomfort could be stemming from the fact that the decision is simply new, not that it is wrong. As Harvard psychiatrist Srinivasan S. Pillay says, if "it doesn't feel 'right,' that may simply be because an old reward system is being disrupted, not because there is something wrong with the new idea."[70] This is particularly important to keep in mind if your company is going through a transition or pursuing a change management strategy.

Impact of Food on Decision-Making

Another bias to be aware of when making decisions is the impact that food has on your decision-making. Beware of making decisions on an empty stomach. Case in point: Researchers analyzed the decisions that parole judges make, looking to see whether a criminal is granted or denied parole. Every day, judges receive cases in random order, and they typically spend about six minutes on each case, approving only 35 percent of the cases.

During the study, researchers noted the exact time of each decision as well as the times of the judges' food breaks—morning break, lunch, and afternoon break. When the researchers analyzed the results, they found that after each meal break, the number of approved parole requests spiked, with judges approving parole 65 percent of the time after a food break. In the two hours after the food break, approvals dropped steadily and reached nearly zero just before the meal. Whether the judges were cranky right before a meal or whether they simply fell back on the default "deny," which makes up 65 percent of the decisions is not clear, but as behavioral psychologist Daniel Kahneman concludes, "Both fatigue and hunger probably play a role."[71]

As this research shows, it's clear that being hungry can impact your decision-making. So be sure that you're eating healthy meals regularly.

10

BRAIN TRAINING APPS

From 2005 to 2007, the brain fitness business industry in the US grew from $100 million to $225 million, according to a report by SharpBrains, a market research company specializing in cognitive health. One reason why the industry is growing is the ability of science, through fMRI and PET scans mentioned earlier, to now investigate the claims that these software programs actually do improve memory or intelligence.

Lumosity

Perhaps most well-known among the brain training firms is Lumosity, which has received investor funding to the tune of $70 million, was the No. 1 app in Apple's AppStore, and a had user base of 25 million as of August 2012.[72]

Lumosity has been aggressively pursuing scientific partnerships and encouraging research on its software-based training programs. Its Lumos Labs published a study demonstrating that normal, healthy adults could use online cognitive training to enhance memory and attention. The findings, published in the *Mensa Research Journal*, showed that participants who did Lumosity training 20 minutes a day for five weeks saw 10 percent improvements in working memory and 20 percent improvements in visual attention. Control participants who didn't train didn't show improvement.

Cognifit

Likewise, a company called Cognifit conducted a two-year clinical trial involving 121 volunteers age 50 and over. Participants either used Cognifit's MindFit or a variety of popular computer games for the allotted time. The results showed that overall, the MindFit group did better than those who played conventional computer games, such as Tetris.[73]

MindFit users experienced significantly greater improvement than the others, namely:

- Short-term memory improved 15 percent
- Simple reaction time improved 19 percent

MindFit is the brainchild of Shlomo Breznitz, a psychologist at the University of Haifa in Israel and CEO of Cognifit. The ideal training regimen is an hour a week, split into three sessions. "If you can increase your short-term memory by one to two items," Breznitz says, "it can be revolutionary in everyday life."[74]

Posit Science

Finally, the Mayo Clinic tested the Brain Fitness Program by Posit Science. Researchers found that the software helped improve test scores across a range of brain functions, according to clinical neuropsychologist Glenn Smith, who led the study.[75] Participants using the software program improved their working memory twice as much as the control group. But, they had to keep at the training to maintain the advantage. After 8 weeks without training, the gains had dropped to 4 percent.

11

BECOMING AN ELITE MENTAL ATHLETE

When we think about improving our performance, we often focus on doing better what we already do. Maybe you regularly engage in continuing education and even make it a point to collect dots—lots of information—both within and outside of your field to encourage connections and creative ideas. Those things are all important. But they aren't enough. We must also train our brains.

The good news is that many of the things discussed in this book are easy: Eat right, sleep more, exercise. Granted, they are also easier said that done. But just like when you figure out how to fit in a graduate-level business course, you can also find a way to work in these important aspects of improving your performance.

Here's a recap of takeaways from each chapter. As you read through, ask yourself: What could you start doing today to prepare yourself to be an elite mental athlete?

Elite Performance

- **Know your brain.** Elite athletes know their bodies and train their bodies; elite mental athletes must know their brains and train their brains. Elite athletes commit serious time to intentional improvement programs, not just haphazard training. They work with a coach, do diagnosis, learn which muscles to work on and how much.

Following the suggestions in the book will help you improve your mental fitness.

- **Train your brain.** It's important to train your brain: It will help you personally, not only in your career but also in your later years, by reducing your risk of Alzheimer's disease and cognitive decline. It will also help your company. If you're a CEO or leader, your mind is the value you are bringing to your company. And, simply put, your competitors will be doing it, even if you aren't.

The Brain: Did You Know?

- **Grow your brain.** Adult brains are malleable—they can grow new brain cells and rewire for efficiency based on training and experience.

- **Expand your memory.** Research shows that even fluid intelligence—that is, brain processing ability, not just the facts you know—can be improved through training that expands working memory and attention.

Nutrition: Feeding Your Mental Machine

- **Drink water.** Drinking right helps you think right. The brain is 75 to 80 percent water, so drinking 8 to 10 glasses of water a day is important to keeping it properly hydrated.

- **Limit caffeine.** Caffeine heightens awareness but is not good for deep thought. Keep consumption below 300 milligrams a day for best results.

- **Get the good fats.** Brain cells depend on fat for construction, repair, and ongoing communications in the brain. Your brain performs best when your intake of fats is a 4:1 ratio between omega-3 and omega-6 fatty acids. Most people get enough omega-6s in their diet. To get omega-3s, look for cold-water fish such as salmon, sardines, herring, anchovies, tuna, and mackerel. Flaxseeds, walnuts, and walnut oil are also good sources of omega-3s.

- **Consume choline.** To improve brain speed and memory, choose foods that contain choline. Foods high in choline include almonds, beef (beef liver is especially high), broccoli, cabbage, egg with yolk, fish, peanuts, and peanut butter. Wheat germ is another especially rich source of choline. Foods high in calcium also boost acetylcholine, so low-fat milk, cheese, and yogurt (especially Greek-style yogurt) are also beneficial.

Exercise: Healthy Body, Healthy Brain

- **Exercise to build your brain.** Aerobic exercise as well as resistance exercise, or strength training, benefits the brain in documented, measurable ways. Exercise changes your brain chemistry, promoting the ability of the brain to remain flexible and rewire itself.

- **Pick aerobic, competitive activities.** Aerobic exercise gets your blood pumping to your brain and can protect against Alzheimer's disease. The more aerobic the exercise, the better: Running is better than walking. Even better, choose a competitive sport or physical activity that involves movements that you're not able to anticipate. For example, basketball, tennis, soccer, and even ping-pong are better than golf or swimming, where the movements are much more predictable as opposed to requiring fast reaction.

- **Make exercise a priority.** If you think you're too busy to exercise, realize that regular exercise raises energy levels 20 percent and leads to less stress, better mood, and improved cognitive functioning. Making 80 hours a week of poor judgments is no way to run a business.

Sleep: The Undervalued Resource

- **Value sleep.** Sleep is undervalued in our culture, but it's the time when the brain does its "back-office paperwork," filing away the day's experiences into long-term memory and making new connections. Although sleep seems like wasted downtime, it's actually an active process vital for mental performance.

- **Perform better when you're awake.** Athletes who sleep more perform better. Students who sleep more get better grades. Executives who get enough rest make better decisions because sleep enhances learning and problem solving.

- **Learn to sleep well.** To get a good night's sleep, follow these tips:

  1) Have a pre-bedtime ritual that you follow every night.
  2) Go to bed at about the same time each night and wake up at about the same time each morning.
  3) Keep a notepad next to your bed to jot down thoughts when your mind is racing.
  4) Use earplugs and sleep shades to ensure a dark, quiet sleep environment.
  5) Avoid TV, computers, and mobile devices an hour before bed.

Stress: The Creativity Killer

- **Avoid prolonged stress.** Stress is part of everyday life, especially if you want to push the limits of performance. But prolonged, unrelenting stress is bad for your body and can damage your brain.

- **Exercise to beat stress.** Exercise is the best way to deal with stress, not just in the short-term but also in the long-term. It has been shown to lead to reductions of more than 50 percent in the prevalence of the symptoms of anxiety.

- **Practice stress-reducing techniques.** Like Felix Baumgartner, use deep breathing, practice positive self-talk, and practice dealing with uncomfortable situations as a way to reduce fear and stress.

Mental Stamina

- **Re-energize by task switching.** When feeling mental fatigue, switch tasks. Simply switching from one task to a different one can re-energize you.

- **Make exercise part of aging.** Exercise promotes mental stamina, even into old age.

Pattern Recognition and Expertise

- **Recognize patterns.** Expertise is based on pattern recognition, which offsets the limits of working memory by creating increasingly larger "chunks" that your mind can handle.

- **Practice to build expertise.** Building expertise requires deliberate practice—pushing yourself beyond your comfort zone to practice not just what you already know, but something you can't do well—or even do at all.

Decision-Making and Cognitive Traps

- **Beware of cognitive traps.** Availability bias, recency bias, anchoring, and framing errors can derail your decisions.

- **Question your gut.** "Gut feel" can be wrong if it's not based on expertise. Your natural wariness in a new situation may cause you to feel a decision is "wrong" simply because it is new.

- **Feed your body regularly.** Being hungry can impact your decision-making, as research on parole judges showed. So be sure that you're eating healthy meals regularly to improve consistency in your decision making.

Sources

1   Excerpted from *Kobe Bryant's Workout Plan* http://www.nbaplayerworkouts.com/kobe-bryant

2   Chris Ballard. *Art of the Beautiful Game: The Thinking Fan's Tour of the NBA New York.* Simon & Schuster/SI Books, 2009

3   Chris Ballard. "The Hoops Whisperer," *Sports Illustrated*, October 26, 2009 http://sportsillustrated. cnn.com/2009/writers/chris_ballard/10/20/idan.ravin/

4   Poldrack, R. A., & Willingham, D. T. "Functional Neuroimaging of Skill Learning," In R. Cabeza & A. Kingstone (Eds.), *Handbook of Functional Neuroimaging of Cognition* (113–148). Cambridge, MA: MIT Press, 2006

5   Wise, R. J. S., & Price, C. J. (2006). "Functional Neuroimaging of Language," In R. Cabeza & A. Kingstone (Eds.), *Handbook of Functional Neuroimaging of Cognition.* Cambridge, MA: MIT Press.

6   Sabrina M. Tom, Craig R. Fox, Christopher Trepel, Russell A. Poldrack. "The Neural Basis of Loss Aversion in Decision Making Under Risk." *Science 26*, January 2007, Vol. 315, 515-518

7   Marie Banich. "Mind and Neuroscience," University of Colorado-Boulder Continuing Education Program held January 26, 2013.

8   Elizabeth Gould. "Stress, Deprivation, and Adult Neurogenesis," In M. S. Gazzaniga (Ed.), *The Cognitive Neurosciences* (139–148). Cambridge, MA: MIT Press, 2004

9   John J. Medina, Diane Coutu. "The Science of Thinking Smarter: A Conversation with Brain Expert John J. Medina," *Harvard Business Review*, May 1, 2008, Vol. 86, Issue 5, 51-54.

10   A. Amedi, A. Floel, S. Knecht, E. Zohary, and L.G. Cohen. "Transcranial Magnetic Stimulation of the Occipital Pole Interferes, With Verbal Processing in Blind Subjects," *Nature Neuroscience* 7, 2004. 1266–1270

11   Cao, Y., Vikingstad, E. M., Huttenlocher, P. R., Towle, V. L., & Levin, D. N. (1994). "Functional Magnetic Resonance Imaging Studies of the Reorganization of the Human Head Sensorimotor Area After Unilateral Brain Injury," *Proceedings of the National Academy of Sciences of the United States of America*, 91, 9612–9616,

12   Edna Sun. "Can Juggling Improve Your Brain?" ABC News, January 26, 2004 http://abcnews.go.com/Health/Technology/story?id=116656&page=1#.TxHl0aU7Vh9

13   John Jonides, Susanne M. Jaeggi, Martin Buschkuehl, Priti Shah. "Building Better Brains," *Scientific American Mind*, September/October 2012, 23, 59-63

14   John Jonides, Susanne M. Jaeggi, Martin Buschkuehl, Priti Shah "Building Better Brains," *Scientific American Mind*, September/October 2012, 23, 59-63

Sources •

15 Lars Bäckman, Lars Nyberg, Anna Soveri, Jarkko Johansson, Micael Andersson, Erika Dahlin, Anna S. Neely, Jere Virta, Matti Laine, Juha O. Rinne. "Effects of Working-Memory Training on Striatal Dopamine Release," *Science 5*, August 2011, Vol. 333, no. 6043, 718 http://www.sciencemag.org/content/333/6043/718.full?sid=50e9c148-290b-4fb9-84f3-205ae19641fe

16 Kaspar Mossman. "Brain Trainers: A Workout for the Mind," *Scientific American*, March 25, 2009 http://www.scientificamerican.com/article.cfm?id=brain-trainers

17 David Glover. http://theeliteproject.com/2011/07/jc_chamberlain_world_record/

18 Cyrus A. Raji, April J. Ho, Neelroop N. Parikshak, James T. Becker, Oscar L. Lopez, Lewis H. Kuller, Xue Hua, Alex D. Leow, Arthur W. Toga, and Paul M. Thompson. "Brain Structure and Obesity," *Human Brain Mapping*, 2009.

19 LT, Haltia Viljanen A, Parkkola R, Kemppainen N, Rinne JO, Nuutila P, Kaasinen V. "Brain White Matter Expansion in Human Obesity and the Recovering Effect of Dieting," *Journal of Clinical Endocrinology and Metabolism*, August 2007, 92 (8), 3278-3284. http://www.ncbi.nlm.nih.gov/pubmed/17536002

20 Paul E. Bendheim. "The Brain Training Revolution: A Proven Workout for Healthy Brain Aging, " *Sourcebooks*, 2009

21 Eric Braverman. *Younger Brain, Sharper Mind.* Emmaus, PA: Rodale, 2011

22 Wayne Weiten. "Perspectives on Psychology," *Cengage Learning*, 2008, 559

23 Virginia Sole-Smith. "All-Day Energy, Every Day," Health.com, December 2012 http://www.cnn.com/2012/12/28/health/health-all-day-energy/

24 Eric Braverman. *Younger Brain, Sharper Mind.* Emmaus, PA: Rodale, 2011

25 Maggie Greenwood-Robinson. *Memory, Mind and Emotions*, Emmaus, PA: Rodale, 2007

26 Cynthia Sass. "The Secret Reason You're Pigging Out," Health.com, January 2013

27 John Ratey and Eric Hagerman. *Spark: The Revolutionary New Science of Exercise and the Brain.* New York: Little, Brown and Company, 2008.

28 "Get Smart," *Scientific American Mind*, May/June 2012, 23, 14.

29 John J. Medina, Diane Coutu. "The Science of Thinking Smarter: A Conversation with Brain Expert John J. Medina," *Harvard Business Review*, May 1, 2008, Vol. 86, Issue 5, 51-54

Sources

30 Laura Chaddock, Mark Neider, Michelle Voss, Jon Gaspar, Arthur Kramer. "Do Athletes Excel at Everyday Tasks?" *Medicine & Science in Sports & Exercise*, October 2011, Vol. 43, Issue 10, 1920-1926 http://journals.lww.com/acsm-msse/Abstract/2011/10000/Do_Athletes_Excel_at_Everyday_Tasks_.14.aspx

31 Eric Braverman. *Younger Brain, Sharper Mind.* Emmaus, PA: Rodale, 2011

32 K. Van der Borght, Kóbor-Nyakas DE, Klauke K, Eggen BJ, Nyakas C, Van der Zee EA, Meerlo P. "Physical Exercise Leads to Rapid Adaptations in Hippocampal Vasculature: Temporal Dynamics and Relationship to Cell Proliferation and Neurogenesis," *Hippocampus.* October 2009, 19 (10), 928-936, http://www.ncbi.nlm.nih.gov/pubmed/19212941

33 Deborah Brauser. "Weight Training, Walking Improve Cognition in the Elderly," *Medscape News Today*, July 15, 2012, http://www.medscape.com/viewarticle/767452

34 Gretchen Reynolds. "Exercise and the Ever-Smarter Human Brain," *New York Times,* December 26, 2012. http://well.blogs.nytimes.com/2012/12/26/exercise-and-the-ever-smarter-human-brain/

35 D.A. Raichlen, James D. Polk. "Linking Brains and Brawn: Exercise and the Evolution of Human Neurobiology," *Proceedings of the Royal Society - Biological Sciences*, January 7, 2013, 280(1750), 20122250, http://www.ncbi.nlm.nih.gov/pubmed/23173208

36 John J. Ratey with Eric Hagerman. *Spark: The Revolutionary New Science of Exercise and the Brain.* New York: Little, Brown, 2008

37 Virginia Sole-Smith. "All-day Energy, Every Day," Health.com, December 28, 2012 http://www.cnn.com/2012/12/28/health/health-all-day-energy/

38 Jonathan Fields. "The Creative Brain On Exercise," *Fast Company*, September 28, 2011 http://www.fastcompany.com/1783263/creative-brain-exercise

39 John R. Ryan. "What Neuroscience Can Teach Leaders," *BusinessWeek,* August 12, 2011 http://www.businessweek.com/management/what-neuroscience-can-teach-leaders-08122011.html

40 James Maas. *Sleep for Success.* AuthorHouse, 2011

41 Erin Allday. "Stanford Athletes Sleep for Better Performance," *San Francisco Chronicle,* July 4, 2011 http://www.sfgate.com/news/article/Stanford-athletes-sleep-for-better-performance-2355759.php#ixzz2JW0dOrsp

42 "Sleeping Longer Helps Athletes Reach Peak Performance," BBC News, July 1, 2011 http://www.bbc.co.uk/news/health-13974130

Sources • • • • • • • • • • • • • • • • • • •

43 Lauren Weber. "Making the Case for Bedtime," *The Wall Street Journal*, January 22, 2013 http://online.wsj.com/article/SB10001424127887323301104578257894191502654. html?google_editors_picks=true

44 Paul E. Bendheim. "The Brain Training Revolution: A Proven Workout for Healthy Brain Aging," *Sourcebooks*, 2009, 257

45 Maquet, P., S. Laureys, P. Peigneux et al. 2000. "Experience-Dependent Changes in Cerebral Activation During Human REM Sleep," *Nat. Neuroscience* 3, 831-836; Maquet, P., S. Schwartz, R. Passingham et al. 2003. "Sleep-Related Consolidation of a Visuo-Motor Skill," *Journal of Neuroscience* 23, 1432-1440

46 Associated Press, "Study Confirms Sleep Essential for Creativity," CNN.com, January 21, 2004

47 Deirdre Barrett. *The Committee of Sleep: How Artists, Scientists, and Athletes Use Their Dreams for Creative Problem Solving—and How You Can Too.* New York: Random House 2001; Oneiroi Press, 2010

48 James Maas. *Sleep for Success.* AuthorHouse, 2011

49 "Extra Sleep Improves Athletes' Performance," *Science Daily*, June 14, 2007 http://www.sciencedaily. com/releases/2007/06/070613071054.htm

50 Erin Allday. "Stanford Athletes Sleep for Better Performance," *San Francisco Chronicle,* July 4, 2011 http://www.sfgate.com/news/article/Stanford-athletes-sleep-for-better-performance-2355759. php#ixzz2JW0dOrsp

51 John J. Medina, Diane Coutu. "The Science of Thinking Smarter: A Conversation with Brain Expert John J. Medina," *Harvard Business Review*, May 1, 2008, Vol. 86, Issue 5, 51-54.

52 David Rock, Jeffrey Schwartz. "Why Neuroscience Matters to Executives," *Strategy and Business*, April 10, 2007 http://www.strategy-business.com/article/li00021?gko=60b7d

53 Mathias Schmid, Lars Schwabe. "Splintered By Stress," *Scientific American Mind* September/October 2011, 22-29.

54 Jonathan Fields. "The Creative Brain On Exercise," *Fast Company*, September 28, 2011 http://www.fastcompany.com/1783263/creative-brain-exercise

55 Michael Gazzaniga, Todd Heatherton, Diane Halpern. *Psychological Science.* 3rd edition, New York: Norton 2009, 102

56 Beth Carter. "How Claustrophobia Almost Grounded Supersonic Skydiver," CNN Tech, October 14, 2012, http://www.cnn.com/2012/10/12/tech/claustrophobia-skydiver

57 Brad Feld. "Mental Stamina for Athletes," *Feld Thoughts*, www.feld.com

Sources

58 John Coates. "Retraining Your Response To Stress and Mental Fatigue," *Fast Company*, June 18, 2012 http://www.fastcompany.com/1840549/retraining-your-response-stress-and-mental-fatigue

59 John Wray. "Haruki Murakami, The Art of Fiction No. 182," *The Paris Review*, 2004 http://www.theparisreview.org/interviews/2/the-art-of-fiction-no-182-haruki-murakami

60 Malcolm Gladwell. *Outliers*. New York: Little, Brown 2008

61 David Levitin. *This Is Your Brain on Music: The Science of a Human Obsession*. New York: Dutton, 2006 p. 197

62 Xiaohong Wan, Hironori Nakatani, Kenichi Ueno, Takeshi Asamizuya, Kang Cheng, Keiji Tanaka. "The Neural Basis of Intuitive Best Next-Move Generation in Board Game Experts," *Science 21*, January 2011, Vol. 331, no. 6015, 341-346 http://www.sciencemag.org/content/331/6015/341. abstract?sid=efa3601b-d089-4e82-91a2-bc121a15204f

63 K. Anders Ericsson, Michael J. Prietula, Edward T. Cokely. "The Making of An Expert," *Harvard Business Review*, July 2007, http://hbr.org/2007/07/the-making-of-an-expert/

64 Malcolm Gladwell. *Outliers*. New York: Little, Brown 2008, 39

65 K. Anders Ericsson, Michael J. Prietula, Edward T. Cokely. "The Making of An Expert," *Harvard Business Review*, July 2007, http://hbr.org/2007/07/the-making-of-an-expert/

66 William Duggan. *Strategic Intuition*. New York: Columbia University Press, 2007.

67 Ellen Di Resta. "Innovation and Neuroscience," chapter in *Global Innovation Science Handbook*. New York: McGraw-Hill, 2013.

68 Sian Beilock. *Choke: What the Secrets of the Brain Reveal About Getting It Right When You Have To*. New York: Free Press, 2011

69 Ali Khounsary. (Argonne National Laboratory) "Driving or Flying?" *Newton* http://www.newton. dep.anl.gov/askasci/gen99/gen99845.htm

70 Srinivasan Pillay. "Relevance of Neuroscience to the Business Environment," *Financial Times*, February 21, 2011 http://www.ftpress.com/articles/article.aspx?p=1645876

71 Daniel Kahneman. *Thinking, Fast and Slow*. New York: Farrar, Straus and Giroux, 2011, 43-44

72 Sarah Kessler. "Brain Games Company Lumosity Is Business Up Front, Experiment in the Back," *Fast Company*, August 28, 2012, http://www.fastcompany.com/3000753/brain-games-company-lumosity-business-front-experiment-back-end

Sources • • • • • • • • • • • • • • • • • • •

73 "Clinical Trial Finds Cognitive Training Software Helps Combat Effects of Depression in Baby Boomers, Seniors," Results Announced at The Alzheimer's Association International Conference on the Prevention of Dementia June 11. http://www.prnewswire.com/news-releases/clinical-trial-finds-cognitive-training-software-helps-combat-effects-of-depression-in-baby-boomers-seniors-58007867.html

74 Kaspar Mossman. "Brain Trainers," *Scientific American Mind*, April/May/June 2009.

75 Robert Goodier. "Do Brain Trainer Games and Software Work?" *Scientific American*, July 2, 2009 http://www.scientificamerican.com/article.cfm?id=brain-trainings-unproven-hype